# SPELLING
# IN CONTEXT

# AGE 9 - 11 YEARS

## Glendra Read

Folens
Publishers

 # CONTENTS

© 1993 Folens Limited, on behalf of the author.

First published 1993 by Folens Limited, Dunstable and Dublin.

Illustrations by Chris Masters          Cover by Graphic Editions

ISBN 185276391-4

**Folens**
*COPYMASTER*

Folens Limited, Apex Business Centre, Boscombe Road, Dunstable, LU5 4RL, England.

# INTRODUCTION

## This book in context

This book is the final part of a series of three linked spelling books. Book 1 of the series is for 5-7-year-olds, and spans National Curriculum Levels 1-3. As well as individual activity sheets, it also has a parents' sheet and a self-evaluation sheet for children. Book 2 is for 7-9-year-olds, and spans National Curriculum Levels 2-4. As well as individual practice sheets, it also has two diagnostic dictations and a diagnostic record sheet. There is some overlap between Books 1 and 2.

Book 3 offers spelling activities for average 9-11-year-olds working from National Curriculum Level 3 onwards. Teachers needing reassurance that their pupils have mastered many of the basic spellings should refer to the word lists at the end of this book, which summarise spellings already covered in Books 1 and 2.

Children aged 9 and over who have specific spelling problems, or who have missed out on early skills acquisition, may need activities from lower National Curriculum Levels and possibly referral to support services for an intensive programme of spelling tuition.

## This book and the National Curriculum

Spelling is Attainment Target 4 in the National Curriculum for English, and spelling should always be seen and used in the wider literary context. This book aims to support teachers working from Level 3 onwards.

**Level 3** of Attainment Target 4 specifies that children should be spelling correctly simple polysyllabic words which follow common patterns. They should understand about vowel sounds and commonly occurring letter strings. Word families should be familiar to them. Language skills such as redrafting and revising are highlighted and regular use of a dictionary is advocated.

**Level 4** encourages study of the main prefixes and suffixes, and states that children should spell correctly words with other main patterns in English spelling.

**Levels 5, 6** and **7** combine the skills of spelling and handwriting into Attainment Target 4/5: "Presentation". Level 5 states that children should be spelling words of greater complexity, checking final drafts of their work, and producing clear, readable handwriting. Level 6 goes into greater depth about words with related meanings (e.g. sign and signature), and emphasises checking of work, legible writing, and the appropriate use of presentational devices such as a computer print-out or desktop publishing. Level 7 specifies study of words with common roots which have been borrowed from other languages (e.g. Latin, Greek, or French) and again emphasises the checking of work, and the careful, attractive presentation of finished work.

## Terminology

The National Curriculum promotes the use of shared language when discussing work with children. It is important that children understand about specific terms denoting parts of speech (e.g. nouns, verbs, etc.), especially when work is being redrafted. For similar reasons, the correct terms - vowels, consonants, syllables, homophones, plurals, synonyms, etc. - are used throughout the series of books, so that teachers and children may have a common frame of reference.

**What is in the book**

Books 1 and 2 cover the basics concerning the importance of vowels, and the usefulness of syllables. Also covered are consonant blends (br, fl, etc.), double vowels (oa, ay, etc.), vowel/consonant digraphs (ur, or, etc.), silent letters l,k,b and w, and certain common letter strings.

This book contains 46 worksheets and does not go over the areas covered in the previous two books. Book 3 begins by looking at basic parts of speech to put spelling into a grammatical context. It moves on to deal with alphabetical order, dictionary work, proofreading, formation of plurals, and more silent letters. The second half of the book investigates where many of our English words come from: Anglo-Saxon, Latin and Greek roots. Then it looks at more complex letter strings such as ew, ue, ui, and aw, au, our. Negative prefixes are considered, and general rules for suffixing outlined, with specific sheets covering 'ful', 'le', 'tion', 'ary' etc. There are two sheets of odd words (such as 'manoeuvre' and 'somersault') and a sheet covering many difficult words with which adults have trouble! The sheets have a varied format to cater for differing tastes.

Finally, there are word lists containing a summary of spellings from Books 1 and 2, and two sheets containing words from this book. In the Appendix, there is a book list including dictionaries, spellcheckers, reference books, thesauri, specialist dictionaries, spelling schemes and computer programs.

**How the book can help with spelling**

Sheets in this book can be used to **teach** a particular spelling point, or to **reinforce** an area taught previously. Sheets can also be used to help children **think** about word derivations and usage, and to **extend** their vocabulary. They can be used with individual children, in groups, or for homework so that children can involve parents in their learning.

**How to teach spelling**

By the age of 9 years, children should know that to learn a new word, they need to use most of their senses. They must **look** carefully at the word, **listen** as the letters are spoken aloud, **write** the word in a flowing handwriting style without further reference to it, and then **check** the completed word with the original. Greater detail about this 'simultaneous oral spelling' method is given in Bryant and Bradley's excellent book (see Appendix).

Some children may be helped by employing syllable breakdown, while others with severe problems may be helped by touching plastic, wooden or cardboard letters and constructing words in a physical manner.

Good spellers use lots of different strategies and methods for working out how to spell words. They may use a combination of any of these methods:

- writing the word in different ways to see which looks right
- visualising the word in the 'mind's eye'
- writing the word quickly without thinking
- thinking about what is the most likely spelling
- breaking the word into syllables
- saying the word to see how it sounds
- thinking of other words with the same pattern (e.g. bruise, cruise)
- thinking of other words with the same root (e.g. locate, dislocate)
- saying the word in an odd way (e.g. skissors to remember the silent c)
- thinking about a little word that lies in a bigger word (e.g. lane in miscellaneous to remember the 'e').

On top of this, good spellers very often benefit because they know they are good spellers! Confidence builds on confidence and confidence grows when children think that they can achieve a target. It may be helpful to talk to children about these methods, and help them to think about what works best for **them**.

**Memory**

Everyone needs a memory bank of spellings. Children must be helped to use their memories effectively, and to get to know where their strengths and weaknesses lie. Some children will be helped by strengthening **visual** links, some by reinforcing **aural** channels, and others may need notes, lists, tricks or spellcheckers to help them. It should be remembered that using a good, flowing writing style will help children through the memory of movement in the writing hand.

### Redrafting/Proofreading

Children should always be encouraged to read through their work to check for misspellings, and to check on content. Most first drafts need to be proofread, but not all of them will need to be re-written. Some will be rewritten for display purposes, or if a piece is to be sent elsewhere (e.g. a letter).

Children can be helped to identify and categorise their own errors, and to note whether, for instance, their errors tend to occur in high frequency words, word beginnings or endings, or if extra letters are put in and others left out. (Book 2 gives two dictation passages and a diagnostic record sheet, though any piece of free writing can be used for diagnostic purposes.)

If one particular aspect of a misspelt word is highlighted for the child's benefit (e.g. fritening - **ght**), then that particular letter string can be taught and learnt.

### Dictionaries

By the age of 9 years, children should be competent at using a dictionary. Dictionaries are useful for checking meanings or spellings, but this activity will be frustrating and laborious for poor spellers. A spellchecker, such as the Franklin Elementary Spellchecker (see Appendix) should be available for children with spelling difficulties (though a reading age of 8+ is necessary to operate the equipment, as any particular word needs to be chosen from a list of similar looking words). Thesauri, specialist dictionaries (like the A.C.E. dictionary - see Appendix), rhyming dictionaries and dictionaries of quotations should also be available.

### Subject-based spellings

Sometimes it is useful to give the class, or a group of children, subject-based 'pre-organiser' words. Such words would be curriculum-based, and should be given to children to learn before a lesson. In geography, words to learn might be terms from AT3 'Physical Geography - land forms' (e.g. valley, mountain, peninsula, erosion, etc.) in science, terms from AT9 'Earth and atmosphere' (e.g. Centigrade, Fahrenheit, isobar, etc.), or in history, terms from the study of Ancient Greece (e.g. myths, Persia, frieze, etc.). The spin-off from this activity would be better spelling in relevant lessons.

The main incentive for children to spell correctly should come from their need or desire to communicate in writing. If children are motivated to write, then they will choose words pertinent to them and their task. Extending their reading horizons will, in turn, widen their spelling vocabulary.

We as teachers can help children in the vital curriculum area of spelling by providing opportunities for language and vocabulary development, and encouraging children to work together to explore word derivations and meanings. We can engender in them an enthusiasm for words, and help them build up a 'word sense' about the English language, consolidating what they do know, and leading them on to become confident, competent spellers for the 21st century.

# Nouns

**Nouns** are naming words.
**Common nouns** name things, like tables or cats (and also abstract things like beauty or anger).
**Proper nouns** name people or places, like **Robin Hood** or **Nottingham**.
**Proper nouns** have capital letters.

The **Queen** went to
**Dublin** in a **car**.

1. In this story, put a line under all the **16 nouns**.

One windy day, a bird flew out from its nest on the cliffs near Dover. Some people had left the remains of a picnic on the beach. The bird swooped and picked up bits of bun, crisps and cake, and flew off with a sandwich for its dinner.

2. In the flags, write the name of the country, next to each associated word, e.g. Danish, Denmark. These are all **proper nouns**. They need **capital letters**.

| | |
|---|---|
| American _____ | Irish _____ |
| British _____ | Italian _____ |
| Canadian _____ | Japanese _____ |
| Egyptian _____ | Kenyan _____ |
| German _____ | Mexican _____ |
| Greek _____ | Norwegian _____ |
| Indian _____ | Spanish _____ |

3. Write the names of nine nouns - things you can see now. These are common nouns. They do not need capital letters.

_____  _____  _____

_____  _____  _____

_____  _____  _____

Name _____  Date _____

# Verbs

Verbs are **doing** words, or **being** words.

It **was** sunny.  We **ran** off and **played** outside.

1. In this story, put a line under all the **12 verbs**.

They went on safari, but the van broke down!
Elephants chased them, snakes dropped on them,
tigers growled at them, giraffes stared at them,
cheetahs ran past them, rhinos pushed them and
alligators snapped at them.  They screamed and
woke up, it was only a dream!

2.  Write the **verbs** you have found.

_____

_____

_____

3. Now think of things that you **can** do, which animals **can't** do.  All these
   words will be **verbs**.  Make a list like this:

I can read. _____      _____

I can _____      _____

_____      _____

_____      _____

**Note:** Every sentence must have a verb in it.

# Adjectives

Adjectives are **describing** words.

A **fat** cat met a **frightened** mouse on
a **cold**, **dark** night.

1. In this story, put a line under all the **14 adjectives**.

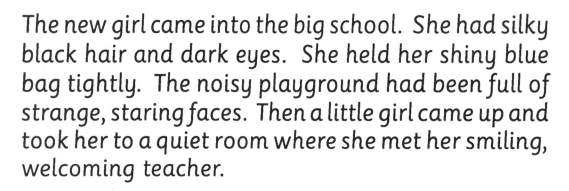

The new girl came into the big school. She had silky
black hair and dark eyes. She held her shiny blue
bag tightly. The noisy playground had been full of
strange, staring faces. Then a little girl came up and
took her to a quiet room where she met her smiling,
welcoming teacher.

2. Write the **adjectives** you have found.

_____

_____

_____

3. **Adjectives** can help you to describe things better. Write down **five**
   **adjectives** to describe each of the following:

a sunset

a rubbish dump

Name _____     Date _____

# Conjunctions

A **conjunction** is a word used to **connect** parts of sentences.

1. Make sure you can read, and spell these conjunctions.  Cover them before you write.

| | | | | | | |
|---|---|---|---|---|---|---|
| or | and | so | but | yet | then | while |

| | | | | |
|---|---|---|---|---|
| however | only | since | therefore | although |

| | | | |
|---|---|---|---|
| because | until | either | neither |

2. Put a **suitable** conjunction in each sentence.

I didn't go out _____ it rained.

John went to the shops _____ Bill stayed in.

This flower is white, _____ this one is red.

I will wait for you _____ 5 o'clock.

The rabbit ate too much, _____ it got fat.

Bill stayed in _____ John went to the shops.

 Make up seven sentences using seven **different** conjunctions.

_____

_____

_____

_____

_____

_____

_____

Name _____  Date _____

# Prepositions

A **preposition** shows how one word relates to another.

**under** the web

**in** the bath

**behind** the plug!

1. Some **prepositions** are quite easy to spell.  Cover each word and spell it.
   Check to see if you are right.

| | | | | | |
|---|---|---|---|---|---|
| of | _____ | down | _____ | in front of | _____ |
| up | _____ | before | _____ | next to | _____ |
| at | _____ | near | _____ | outside | _____ |
| on | _____ | with | _____ | against | _____ |
| in | _____ | over | _____ | across | _____ |
| by | _____ | after | _____ | behind | _____ |
| to | _____ | under | _____ | through | _____ |
| out | _____ | below | _____ | between | _____ |
| for | _____ | inside | _____ | towards | _____ |
| above | _____ | around | _____ | from | _____ |

2. Put a different **preposition** into each sentence.

My dog was running _____ the house.
Suddenly she went _____ the road.  Soon she
went _____ the trees.  Quickly I ran _____
her.  I chased her _____ a pond.  She left the
pond and went _____ the supermarket.  She
ran _____ the meat counter!  Quickly, I got a
bone and rushed _____ the cash desk.  I ran
home and put the bone _____ her basket.
She followed me, and sat _____ me to enjoy
her bone.

Look at the list of prepositions.
Find the **opposites** for as many as you can.
Turn over and write the pairs of words.

Name _____  Date _____

# Adverbs

An **adverb** goes with a verb to say **how** something is done. 'She performed **excellently**.' Many adverbs end in ...ly. 'Fast' and 'well' are two common adverbs that do **not** end in **ly**.

| sorts of spellings | what to add | example |
|---|---|---|
| most adjectives | add  ly | nicely |
| words ending in l | add  ly | hopefully |
| words ending in le | take off e, add y | humbly |
| words ending in y | change y to i, add ly | happily |

Using the chart to help you, write the **adverbs** from these adjectives.

sudden _____     clever _____

wonderful _____     patient _____

deep _____     shiny _____

haughty _____     gracious _____

impossible _____     simple _____

original _____     usual _____

brave _____     single _____

beautiful _____

anxious _____

wise _____

gentle _____

lucky _____

able _____

**Note**: There are four main exceptions:
*true - truly, due - duly, full - fully, dull - dully*

 Turn over and put ten adverbs into sentences.

Name _____     Date _____

# Alphabetical order

The police use certain words to represent letters of the alphabet when spelling names.  If the name SHAW had to be spelt, this would be spelt out 'Sierra', 'Hotel', 'Alpha', 'Whisky', over the radio.

1. Put the words in alphabetical order to complete the police alphabet.

| Yankee | Golf | Zebra | November | Quebec | Hotel | Sierra |
|--------|------|-------|----------|--------|-------|--------|
| Juliet | Papa | Bravo | Echo | Delta | Uncle | Charlie |
| Romeo | Lima | India | Whisky | Alpha | Mike | |
| Victor | X-ray | Tango | Kilo | Oscar | Foxtrot | |

| | | | |
|---|---|---|---|
| A | H | O | V |
| B | I | P | W |
| C | J | Q | X |
| D | K | R | Y |
| E | L | S | Z |
| F | M | T | |
| G | N | U | |

2. Write your name using the police alphabet.

_____

3. You **need** to know the order of letters in the alphabet to use a phone book or dictionary.  Do this part with a friend.  Time the task and see who can do it the quickest.  Write the letters that come **before** and **after** the given letter, e.g. **c** d **e**.

| _ b _ | _ g _ | _ p _ | _ f _ | _ m _ | _ w _ |
|-------|-------|-------|-------|-------|-------|
| _ e _ | _ n _ | _ o _ | _ k _ | _ t _ | _ q _ |
| _ r _ | _ c _ | _ l _ | _ s _ | _ f _ | _ y _ |

Turn over and write the alphabet down the page.
Think of an occupation and description for each letter.
e.g. **A** agile   acrobat
**B** busy   bee-keeper

Do this with a friend and see who completes their list first!

Name _____     Date _____

# Dictionary work

Find three unusual words in the dictionary. Write out each
word with its **correct** definition. Make up two more
definitions for your words. The class, the group, or
your partner has to guess which is the correct
definition, and which are the false ones.

e.g., a) osmium - a drug for treating colds
     b) osmium - a grey-coloured metallic element
     c) osmium - a pink-coloured gas

((b) is the correct definition)

**words**               **definitions (meanings)**

a _____     _____

b _____     _____

c _____     _____


a _____     _____

b _____     _____

c _____     _____


a _____     _____

b _____     _____

c _____     _____

**NOW**    These six words mean **similar** things. Look up their meanings in
a dictionary to find how they are **different** from each other.

pair _____

brace _____

partner _____

couple _____

twins _____

duo _____

   

Name _____   Date _____

# Proofreading - 'double trouble'

Look at the pairs of words.
One spelling in each pair is correct.
Underline the **correct** spelling and write the word
on the line next to the pair.  If you are not sure,
check in a dictionary.

always
allways          _____

wellcome
welcome          _____

rabbit
rabit            _____

radish
raddish          _____

girafe
giraffe          _____

gallop
galopp           _____

tariff
tarrif           _____

teriffic
terrific         _____

ballast
balast           _____

ballance
balance          _____

across
accross          _____

adress
address          _____

parallel
paralel          _____

harass
harrass          _____

embarass
embarrass        _____

develop
developp         _____

necessary
neccessary       _____

exaggerate
exagerate        _____

occur
occurr           _____

instalment
installment      _____

impossible
imposible        _____

abreviate
abbreviate       _____

acommodate
accommodate      _____

recommend
reccommend       _____

# Letter strings

Many words can be learnt because they have letter strings or letter patterns in them which are in other words too: **c**atch/**m**atch/**p**atch/**w**atch.

1. Find the letter strings common to each group of words. Work out the missing word by using the letter strings from the other words in the group.

e.g. ac**tion**
     dic**tion**ary     s t a t i o n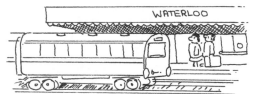
     sec**tion**

1. creature
   adventurer
   future
   p _ _ _ _ _ _

2. flight
   laughter
   brought
   l _ _ _ _ _ _ _

3. hunchback
   bench
   luncheon
   p _ _ _ _ _ _ _

4. swallow
   owing
   slowness
   w _ _ _ _ _
   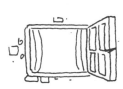

5. bandages
   page
   cottage
   l _ _ _ _ _ _

6. terrible
   bless
   jumble
   t _ _ _ _
   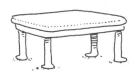

7. drawer
   claws
   lawyer
   j _ _ _ _ _
   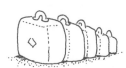

8. cyclone
   unicyclist
   tricycle
   b _ _ _ _ _ _

2. Find three words which contain each of the following letter strings.

*ere* _____    *ake* _____

_____    _____

*own* _____    *ind* _____

_____    _____

   

Name _____    Date _____

# Serial probability

Certain letters tend to go together in a particular language. We need to know that certain combinations of letters occur in English, and that others do not. This is called serial probability.

Look at these nonsense words:

butwenchpt
orqableg
terrially
pifjeries

Which one **looks like an English word**?

You should have chosen **terrially**, because the other three contain letter combinations that do not occur in English ('**chpt**', '**qa**' and '**fj**')

Find the **one word** in each group that looks like an English word. Put a ring round **one word** in each group.

roxhitii
findler
enpodooz
woljfree

trvessain
qotemreff
implorant
lecwentl

haxipenp
nigtrentev
sencbaj
bottages

pvubixe
antitance
mojifureb
wikkrame

crange
thenkp
oksibli
yenmd

mexdyh
lervobj
ligorick
byrrorq

 **NOW**    Lewis Carroll in *Alice Through The Looking Glass* wrote

'Twas brillig and the slithy toves,
Did gyre and gimble in the wabe;
All mimsy were the borogroves,
And the mome raths outgrabe.

Turn over, and write a short story or poem about some fantasy creatures. They could be called 'magniferous splendibles'. Make **some** of the words look strange, but make them **look like English words**. To set yourself even more of a task, try making the story exactly **100 words** long!

# Syllables

A **syllable** is one short word, or part of a longer word.

cat = one syllable

rab bit = two syllables

el e phant = three syllables

1. In this puzzle there are 12 words.  Each word has 3 syllables.  Follow the
   lines from left to right to find the words.  Write the words on the lines.

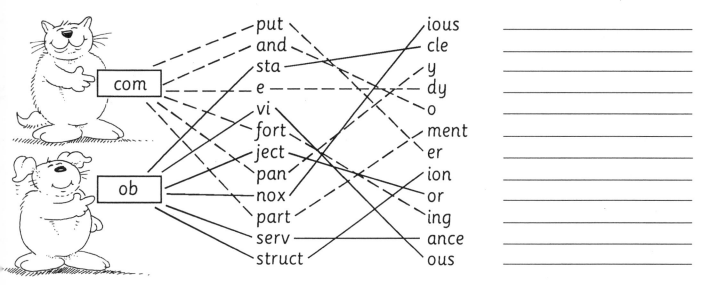

```
com          put          ious        _____
             and          cle         _____
             sta          y           _____
             e            dy          _____
             vi           o           _____
             fort         ment        _____
ob           ject         er          _____
             pan          ion         _____
             nox          or          _____
             part         ing         _____
             serv         ance        _____
             struct       ous         _____
```

2. Breaking longer words into syllables may help you to spell the words.  Try
   putting these syllables together to make words.  Write the words below.

ad ⁓ven⁓ ture.     ad ⁓ver⁓ tise ⁓ment.     con ⁓ di ⁓ tion.

con ⁓cen⁓ tra ⁓ tion.     con ⁓ tam ⁓in⁓ a ⁓ tion.

pro ⁓duc⁓ tion.     pro ⁓ clam ⁓ a ⁓ tion.

pro ⁓fess⁓ ion ⁓ al ⁓ ly.     pro ⁓ nounce ⁓ ment.

_____    _____    _____

_____    _____    _____

_____    _____    _____

Name _____  Date _____

# Plurals 1

**Singular** means **one**. **Plural** means **more than one**.

| sorts of spellings | what to add | example |
|---|---|---|
| most nouns | add **s** | dogs |
| nouns ending in ss, s, z, x, ch, sh | add **es** | foxes |
| nouns ending in a consonant and y | change **y** to **ies** | lorries |
| nouns ending in ay, ey, oy, uy | add **s** | monkeys |
| nouns ending in f, and some in fe | change **f** to **ves** | shelves |
| nouns ending in a vowel plus o (eo, io, oo) | add **s** | radios |
| most other nouns ending in o | add **es** | potatoes |

Using the chart to help you, write the plurals of these nouns:

| house | _____ | donkey | _____ | bush | _____ |
|---|---|---|---|---|---|
| leaf | _____ | church | _____ | knife | _____ |
| boy | _____ | city | _____ | gas | _____ |
| domino | _____ | thief | _____ | battery | _____ |
| studio | _____ | tomato | _____ | magnet | _____ |
| runaway | _____ | elephant | _____ | kangaroo | _____ |

**Note**: There are some exceptions to these rules! Make sure you learn them. Turn over and practise.

- Nouns ending in o which are musical terms add **s** - **pianos, solos, sopranos**.
- Some other nouns also just add **s** - **twos, halos, tobaccos, photos, commandos, embryos, tangos**.
- Some words ending in **f**, just add **s** - **gulfs, proofs, chiefs, roofs, beliefs, dwarfs, griefs**.

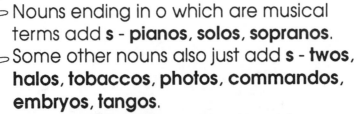

Name _____  Date _____

# Plurals 2

**Singular** means **one**.  **Plural** means **more than one**.

1. Using what you have learned write the plurals of these nouns:

march _____  lady  _____  mattress _____

waltz _____  memory _____  wolf  _____

echo  _____  valley _____  pocket  _____

life  _____  family _____  video  _____

**Note**: There are some more exceptions to these rules!
Make sure you learn them.  Turn over and practise.

 A few words can be spelt **os** or **oes** - **mottos/
mottoes; grottos/grottoes; stilettos/stilettoes;
volcanos/volcanoes; halos/haloes; banjos/banjoes.**
A few words can be spelt **fs** or **ves** - **hoofs/hooves;
turfs/ turves; wharf/wharves; scarfs/scarves.**
Some words stay the same!
**aircraft; cannon; deer; grouse; salmon; sheep.**

2. Some nouns change altogether in the plural.
   Match up the pairs of words.  The first one is done for you.

|  | singular |  | plural |
|---|---|---|---|
| mouse | _____mice_____ | | geese |
| goose | _____ | | women |
| man | _____ | | men |
| tooth | _____ | | children |
| ox | _____ | | teeth |
| woman | _____ | | feet |
| die | _____ | | ~~mice~~ |
| child | _____ | | dice |
| foot | _____ | | oxen |

Some foreign words are strange.  Turn over and try these:

cactus  - cacti        oasis    - oases
medium  - media        gateau   - gateaux
crisis  - crises       plateau  - plateaux
fungus  - fungi        formula  - formulae

Name _____     Date _____

# Collective nouns

Sometimes we need a particular naming word for groups of things.  These are called collective nouns.
e.g. a **troop** of soldiers.

Finish off each phrase by using one of the words on the right.
The first one is done for you.

| | | | |
|---|---|---|---|
| A | flock | of | sheep |
| A | fleet | of | _____ |
| A | crowd | of | _____ |
| A | herd | of | _____ |
| A | babble | of | _____ |
| A | bunch | of | _____ |
| A | pod | of | _____ |
| A | team | of | _____ |
| A | school | of | _____ |
| A | pride | of | _____ |
| A | pack | of | _____ |
| A | swarm | of | _____ |
| A | squadron | of | _____ |
| A | library | of | _____ |
| A | wardrobe | of | _____ |
| A | clump | of | _____ |
| A | ream | of | _____ |
| A | choir | of | _____ |
| A | crew | of | _____ |
| A | gang | of | _____ |

cattle
voices
footballers
sheep
books
ships
fish
sailors
whales
wolves
flowers
clothes
paper
aeroplanes
trees
bees
singers
people
thieves
lions

On your own, or with a friend, use your imagination to think up some new collective nouns for these:

A _____ of clocks          A _____ of sweets
A _____ of teachers        A _____ of robots
A _____ of hamsters        A _____ of garden gnomes
A _____ of racing cars     A _____ of fleas
A _____ of skyscrapers     A _____ of dinosaurs

Name _____  Date _____

# Synonyms

Synonyms are words which have similar meanings.

happy     pleased     merry     jolly     glad

1. Here are ten words with similar meanings to **little**.
   Read the words, then cover them and spell them.

| small | petite | _____ | _____ |
| minute | puny | _____ | _____ |
| tiny | short | _____ | _____ |
| diminutive | microscopic | _____ | _____ |
| miniature | squat | _____ | _____ |

A thesaurus can help you find a good word or phrase for your work.

2. Use a thesaurus to find ten words with similar meanings to **big**.

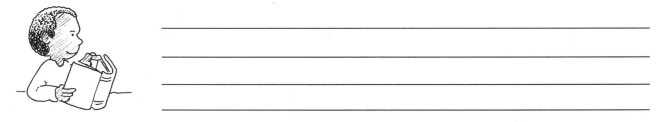

_____
_____
_____
_____

3. Here are ten words with similar meanings to **happy**.
   Read the words, then cover them and spell them.

| pleased | enchanted | _____ |
| merry | delighted | _____ |
| jolly | fascinated | _____ |
| glad | ecstatic | _____ |
| overjoyed | blest | _____ |

 Use a thesaurus again to find ten words with similar meanings to **sad**. Turn over and write your list.

Name _____ Date _____

# Spell **OW** words

Sometimes **o** and **w** go together to make a long **o** sound as in **bow** or arr**ow**.

1. Read this account of a journey.  Underline the 18 **ow** words.
   The first one is done for you.

The <u>flow</u> of traffic from Glasgow had been slow. The temperature was below zero, and snow had begun to fall and get blown into hollows. Looking out of the narrow van windows, they could see the shadows of growing snowdrifts.  At last they saw some yellow lights glowing.  They stopped and followed the driver inside the cafe for bowls of hot soup. Who knows, perhaps the sun would shine tomorrow!

2. Write the **ow** words you have found.

_____

_____

_____

_____

| Add **b, cr, fl, gr, l, m, r, s, sl, sn** and **t** to **ow** to make new words. | From the root word **know** we can make: knows, knowing, knowledge, unknowing, knew.  Do the same sort of thing with the word **grow**. |
| --- | --- |
| _____ | _____ |
| _____ | _____ |
| _____ | _____ |
| _____ | _____ |
| _____ | _____ |
| _____ | _____ |

# Spell qu words

In English **q** is always followed by **u** - **qu**.

**qu** nearly always says 'kw'.

but **que** at the **end** of a word says 'k'.

1. Read these words.

| | | | | |
|---|---|---|---|---|
| queen | squeak | question | squash | equal |
| grotesque | cheque | square | squint | quiet |
| squirrel | quick | squeeze | earthquake | |
| squid | unique | picturesque | antique | |
| technique | | | | |
| quite | quest | squirt | physique | mosque |

2. Sort the words into the three balloons according to whether they start
   with **squ**, end with **que**, or have **qu** in them.  Use each word only once.

**squ**        **que**        **qu**

Look in a dictionary to find the meaning of the word
'quixotic'.  Where does it come from?

Name _____  Date _____

# Spell **ph** words

**p** and **h** together always says '**f**',

as in ele**ph**ant  and tele**ph**one.

1. Write the correct **ph** word next to its meaning.

| | | |
|---|---|---|
| Letters from A-Z | _____ | phantom |
| A game bird | _____ | triumph |
| A solid ball | _____ | sphere |
| An apparition | _____ | geography |
| A large grey animal | _____ | pharaohs |
| A great success | _____ | orphan |
| Rulers of Ancient Egypt | _____ | telephone |
| Child with dead parents | _____ | pheasant |
| Study of the earth's surface | _____ | elephant |
| Instrument for making calls | _____ | alphabet |

2. '**graph**' means '**a thing written or drawn**'. Use a dictionary to find the meanings of these words.

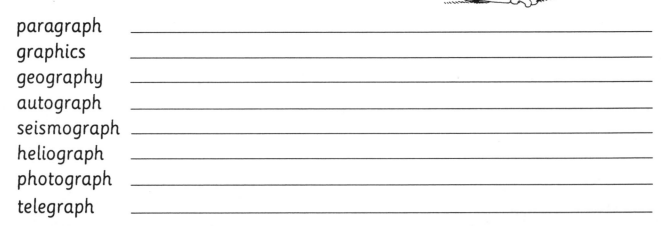

paragraph _____

graphics _____

geography _____

autograph _____

seismograph _____

heliograph _____

photograph _____

telegraph _____

Turn over and find as many words as possible (three letters or more) out of PHOTOGRAPHER.

30+ = **good**
50+ = **very good!**

# Spell ea words

Sometimes **e** and **a** go together to make a short **e** sound, as in **feather** and **head**.

1. Read the story.  Put a line under all the 15 words where **ea** makes a short **e** sound.

It had been dreadful weather with heavy rain.  Many dead leaves had fallen.  Now there was not a breath of wind and the sun shone steadily on the meadow.  It was very pleasant. Heather had her breakfast of bread spread with jam, and got ready to go out for a healthy walk.  It was a pleasure to be out instead of being stuck indoors.

2. Write the short **ea** words you have found.

_____

_____

_____

3. Add **d, h, l, r, tr, br** and **spr** to **ead** to make new words.

_____  _____  _____  _____

_____  _____  _____

**NOW** Turn over and find as many words as possible (three letters or more, and no plurals) out of MEASUREMENT.

**30+ = good**
**50+ = very good!**

Name _____ Date _____

# Spell **gu** words

Sometimes **u** acts as a wall to stop **g** going soft and saying '**j**'.

 **gu**itar     **Gu**ide dog

1. Read the story.
   Put a line under all the nine **gu** words.

Guy needed guidance in his quest for a pet. Reptiles were in vogue. He looked in a catalogue with a colleague and had a vague idea he'd like something furry. He decided on a guinea pig. "I guess I'll have to sell my guitar to get it," he said.

2. Write the **gu** words you have found.

_____

_____

3. Use a dictionary to find the meanings of these words.
   Write them down.

prologue _____
epilogue _____
rogue _____
dialogue _____
disguise _____
guillotine _____
guarantee _____

**Note**: **Language** is an odd **gu** word where **gu** says '**gw**'.

Name _____   Date _____

# Silent letters 1

Of the 26 letters of the alphabet, only five are never silent: **f  j  q  v  x**

The other 21 letters are silent at one time or another **but** they still have to be written!

1. **b, c, n** and **t** are **sometimes** silent.
   Read these words.  The silent letters are **underlined**.

| |
|---|
| bom<u>b</u>     s<u>c</u>issors     mus<u>c</u>le     bus<u>t</u>le          colum<u>n</u><br> castle        thumb         autum<u>n</u><br> thi<u>s</u>tle   climb      whi<u>s</u>tle   de<u>b</u>t      s<u>c</u>ene<br> hym<u>n</u><br> condem<u>n</u>   s<u>c</u>ience      dou<u>b</u>t   lis<u>t</u>en   solem<u>n</u>   as<u>c</u>end |

2. Look carefully at the words you have just read.
   Sort the words according to their silent letters.

| silent **b** | silent **c** | silent **n** | silent **t** |
|---|---|---|---|
| (after m, before t) | (after s) | (after m) | (after s) |
| _____ | _____ | _____ | _____ |
| _____ | _____ | _____ | _____ |
| _____ | _____ | _____ | _____ |
| _____ | _____ | _____ | _____ |
| _____ | _____ | _____ | _____ |

3. **Silent h.** **h** can be silent at the start of a word (hour, honest, heir).  **h** can be silent with c (Christmas), with r (rhino), or with w (white).

 Turn over and draw three boxes, about 5 cm x 10 cm.
Label the boxes **ch, rh,** and **wh.**
Look in a dictionary to find words beginning with **ch, rh,** and **wh, where the h is silent.**  Fill the three boxes with words.

# Silent letters 2

Some letters are always silent with other letters.
**k** is always silent before **n**
**g** is always silent with **n**, at the start of a word
**w** is always silent with **r**

1. Read these words.  The silent letters are **underlined**.

| | | | | | |
|---|---|---|---|---|---|
| <u>w</u>rench | <u>k</u>nock | <u>w</u>riter | <u>w</u>rist | <u>g</u>nu | <u>k</u>nitting |
| <u>k</u>night | <u>w</u>riggle | <u>k</u>nob | <u>g</u>nash | <u>w</u>rinkle | |
| <u>w</u>reath | <u>w</u>reck | <u>w</u>rong | <u>k</u>nuckle | <u>g</u>narled | |
| <u>w</u>rap | <u>k</u>nee | | | | |
| <u>g</u>nat | <u>w</u>rite | <u>g</u>nome | <u>k</u>now  <u>g</u>naw | <u>w</u>restle | <u>w</u>ren |

2. Look carefully at the words you have just read.
   Sort the words according to their silent letters.

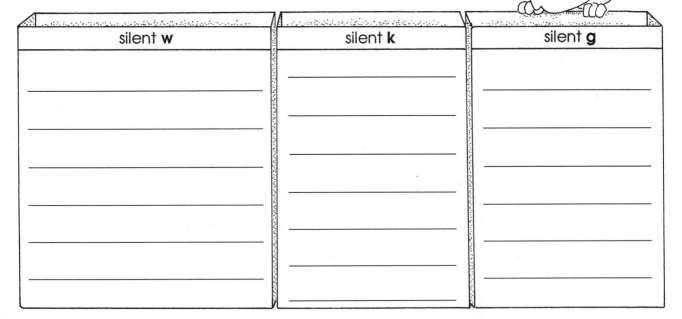

| silent **w** | silent **k** | silent **g** |
|---|---|---|
| _____ | _____ | _____ |
| _____ | _____ | _____ |
| _____ | _____ | _____ |
| _____ | _____ | _____ |
| _____ | _____ | _____ |
| _____ | _____ | _____ |
| _____ | _____ | _____ |

3. **P** is always silent with n, s and t.  These words come from Greek, and are
   **tricky**!  Cover up each word and try to spell it.  Look up their
   meanings in a dictionary if you do not know them.

    pneumonia      psalm      psychology      pterodactyl

    _____    _____    _____    _____

Name _____  Date _____

 # Anglo-Saxon words

| ᚠ | ᚢ | ᚦ | ᚩ | ᚱ | ᚻ | ᚷ | ᚹ | ᚾ | ᚻ |
|---|---|---|---|---|---|---|---|---|---|
| f | u | th | o | r | c | g | w | h | n |

| ᛁ | ᛄ | ᛈ | ᛉ | ᛋ | ᛏ | ᛒ | ᛖ | ᛗ | ᛚ |
|---|---|---|---|---|---|---|---|---|---|
| i | j | p | z | s | t | b | e | m | l |

| ᛜ | ᛟ | ᛞ | · | ᚪ | ᚫ | ᚣ | ᛠ | ᛣ |
|---|---|---|---|---|---|---|---|---|
| ng | oe | d | · | a | ae | y | ea | k |

The Angles and the Saxons invaded the British Isles in AD449. They called their new country 'Englaland' and their writing 'Englisc'. The Anglo-Saxons brought their own writing with them. The letters were called 'runes'.

1. Write your names in runes. _____

2. In a dictionary, '**OE**' shows which words are Old English, or Anglo-Saxon. These words date from about AD500-1200. Read them out loud first then translate these Anglo-Saxon words into Modern English.

| Old English | Modern English |
|---|---|
| *family words* | |
| moder | |
| faeder | |
| sweoster | |
| brothor | |
| sunu | |
| dohter | |
| *food* | |
| milc | |
| buture | |
| cese | |
| mete | |
| fisc | |
| *kitchen utensils* | |
| cuppe | |
| spon | |
| forca | |
| glaes | |
| chif | |

| Old English | Modern English |
|---|---|
| *colours* | |
| blew | |
| read | |
| hwit | |
| brun | |
| grene | |
| geolo | |
| silfer | |
| *animals* | |
| hors | |
| gat | |
| docga | |
| mus | |
| wulf | |
| sceap | |
| pigga | |
| cu | |
| wesule | |

Check in a dictionary to see if you are right!

Name _____    Date _____

# Latin-based words

Latin was the language spoken and written by the Romans.  England was invaded by the Romans between 55BC and AD400, but it wasn't until the Christian religion was established in AD650 that the Roman alphabet was introduced and language and writing changed.  Latin provided thousands of new words and parts of words.  In a dictionary, 'L' shows when a word has Latin roots.

1.  Here are some Latin words and their meanings.  Find English words that come from these Latin roots.  Use a dictionary.

| Latin word | Meaning | English words |
|---|---|---|
| aqua | water | aquarium aquatic aqueduct |
| audio | I hear | |
| centum | a hundred | |
| circa | about | |
| facio | I make/do | |
| finis | an end | |
| liber | free | |
| navis | a ship | |
| octo | eight | |
| primus | first | |
| rota | a wheel | |
| scribo | I write | |
| specto | I watch | |

2.  These Latin phrases are still used today.
    Use a dictionary to find their meanings.

Anno Domini (AD) _____

et cetera (etc.) _____

nota bene (NB) _____

post script (PS) _____

status quo _____

ante meridiem (a.m.) _____

post meridiem (p.m.) _____

Name _____    Date _____

 # Greek-based words

When Constantinople was conquered by the Turks in 1453, a great number of Greek manuscripts came over to the western world. By Elizabethan times, the study of Greek was well established.

In a dictionary, '**Gk**' or '**Gr**' shows when a word has Greek roots.

1. Here are some Greek words and their meanings. Find English words that come from these Greek roots. Use a dictionary.

| Greek word | Meaning | English words |
|---|---|---|
| anti | against | antiseptic   antisocial |
| astro | 'astron' - a star | |
| auto | 'autos' - self | |
| biblio | 'biblion' - book | |
| dia | between | |
| geo | 'ge' - the earth | |
| hydro | 'hydor' - water | |
| hyper | beyond | |
| macro | 'makros' - large | |
| mega | 'megas' - great | |
| micro | 'mikros' - small | |
| mono | 'monos' - alone | |
| neo | 'neos' - new | |
| penta | 'pente' - five | |
| photo | 'phos' - light | |
| poly | 'polys' - many | |
| theo | 'theos' - god | |

2. Some words ending in **ic** come from the Greek.
   Use a dictionary to find the meanings of these words.

authentic _____

acrostic _____

cosmetic _____

drastic _____

frantic _____

Name _____   Date _____

 # Words from France

From 1066 to 1500, over 10,000 words came into the English Language from France.  French scribes brought the 'qu' into English, instead of 'cw'.

1. Many words ending in **et** come from the French.  Some words are pronounced '**it**' (sock**et**), some '**et**' (minu**et**), some '**ay**' (ber**et**).  Read these words.  Sort them according to whether they are pronounced **it** or **ay** in the end syllable.

| trumpet | duvet | cabaret | ticket |
|---------|-------|---------|--------|
| ballet | buffet | croquet | sachet |
| picket | banquet | scarlet | bracket |
| cricket | blanket | ricochet | bouquet |

| 'it' in the end syllable | 'ay' in the end syllable |
|--------------------------|--------------------------|
| _____  _____ | _____  _____ |
| _____  _____ | _____  _____ |
| _____  _____ | _____  _____ |
| _____  _____ | _____  _____ |

2. These French words are used in English.  Look up their meanings in a dictionary.  '**F**' shows when a word comes from France.  Write the meanings.

chauffeur _____

crêpe _____

fête _____

dessert _____

bonbon _____

souvenir _____

roulette _____

promenade _____

moustache _____

silhouette _____

Name _____ Date _____

# Words from other languages

There are over 2,700 languages in the world. English has the largest and most varied vocabulary. Words have come into the English language from all over the world.

1. Here are some **Italian** and **Spanish** words. The Italian words are to do with music and the arts, the Spanish words are to do with the activities of the Spanish explorers. Sort the words into the correct boxes. Look up the word in the dictionary if you are not sure. '**It**' - Italian, '**Sp**' - Spanish.

| piano | pawpaw | tomato | banana | prima donna | ballerina |
| tobacco | potato | opera | galleon | chocolate | hurricane |
| soprano | tempo | aria | violin | tornado | oratorio |

| Italian words | Spanish words |
|---|---|
| _____ _____ | _____ _____ |
| _____ _____ | _____ _____ |
| _____ _____ | _____ _____ |
| _____ _____ | _____ _____ |
| _____ | _____ |

2. Here are some words from **India.** Put the right word next to its meaning

| A one-storey house | _____ | pyjamas |
| A sleeping suit | _____ | verandah |
| Open gallery on side of house | _____ | shampoo |
| To wash and clean hair | _____ | bungalow |
| Dull brownish-yellow colour | _____ | khaki |

3. Look in a dictionary to find the country of origin of these words.

sofa _____
pizza _____
karate _____
patio _____

toboggan _____
judo _____
oasis _____
tomahawk _____

Name _____  Date _____

# Spell **ough** and **augh** words

In Old English, words which now have **gh** in them were spelt with `h` and the `h` was pronounced: ni**h**t (night), tho**h**t (thought). In 1476, William Caxton set up the first English printing press. He had trained in Holland, and his Dutch printers added a `g` to the `h` to make `gh`. They also used `gh` to make the `f` sound in some words. So now we have **laugh** and **rough**!

1. The **gh** words on this page have been grouped where the words are **pronounced** the same way. Cover the words and write them again.

| ough = f | |
|---|---|
| cough | _____ |
| enough | _____ |
| rough | _____ |
| tough | _____ |
| trough | _____ |

| ough = or | |
|---|---|
| bought | _____ |
| brought | _____ |
| fought | _____ |
| nought | _____ |
| ought | _____ |
| sought | _____ |
| thought | _____ |

| ough = oo (as in zoo) | |
|---|---|
| through | _____ |
| throughout | _____ |

| ought = ow (as in cow) | |
|---|---|
| bough | _____ |
| drought | _____ |
| plough | _____ |

| augh = f | |
|---|---|
| laugh | _____ |
| laughing | _____ |
| laughter | _____ |
| draught | _____ |
| draughty | _____ |

| augh = or | |
|---|---|
| caught | _____ |
| daughter | _____ |
| distraught | _____ |
| haughty | _____ |
| naughty | _____ |
| slaughter | _____ |
| taught | _____ |

| ough = u (as in up) | |
|---|---|
| borough | _____ |
| thorough | _____ |

| ough = o (as in go) | |
|---|---|
| doughnut | _____ |
| though | _____ |
| although | _____ |

2. These are much used words:
   bought, brought, thought, laugh
   caught, through.
   Turn over and put these six words
   into six sentences.

# Spell ie words

In shorter words, **ie** often makes a long **i** sound as in **tie**, **die**, **cried**, etc.

In longer words, remember this rule:

I before E, except after C
When the **IE** rhymes with **me**.

1. **ie** *can follow* **c**, *but then it does not make an* **ee** *sound. It says* **sh**, *or the* **c** *is silent.*
Read these words. Then cover them and write them.

proficient _____    conscience _____

sufficient _____    ancient _____

efficient _____    science _____

deficient _____    scientific _____

2. Read this report. Put a line under all the **ie** words.

The chief briefly laid siege to the abbey, to try to retrieve his niece. He had a belief that the priests would yield. He had a shield that could not be pierced, and he looked fierce standing in the field. The priests gave a shriek of grief as a thief achieved his goal and retrieved the chief's niece. There was relief all round when the chief offered the priests a piece of land, and promised no more mischief!

3. Write the **ie** words you have found.

_____

_____

_____

Name _____    Date _____

# Spell **ei** words

I before **E**, except after **C**
When the **IE** rhymes with **me**

1. Read the rule.  Read these **ei** words.  Then cover them and spell them.

receive _____    perceive _____
receipt _____    conceive _____
deceive _____    conceit _____
deceit _____    ceiling _____

2. **Exceptions**
   Although these words rhyme with **me**, they are spelt **ei**. Read, cover and spell them.

seize _____    caffeine _____
seizure _____    either _____
weird _____    neither _____
protein _____    weir _____

3. These **ei** words are pronounced in various ways.  Put the right **ei** word next to its meaning.

Measurement from top to base _____    counterfeit

From another country _____    leisure

To find the weight of _____    sovereign

This takes blood to the heart _____    weigh

A deer with large antlers _____    foreign

Forged (money) _____    vein

Quilt _____    reindeer

Free time _____    neighbour

Supreme ruler _____    height

Person who lives nearby _____    eiderdown

Name _____  Date _____

# Spell ew ue ui words

ew, ue, and ui can make an oo sound.
**Sue** spilt **stew** on the **fruit**.

1. Read these words.

| grew | screw | threw | news | jewel | view | cue |
|------|-------|-------|------|-------|------|-----|
| clue | bruise | cruise | recruit | due | true | juice |
| fruit | blue | glue | knew | few | suit | |

2. Sort the words into the three fruits according to whether they have **ew**,
   **ue**, or **ui** in them.

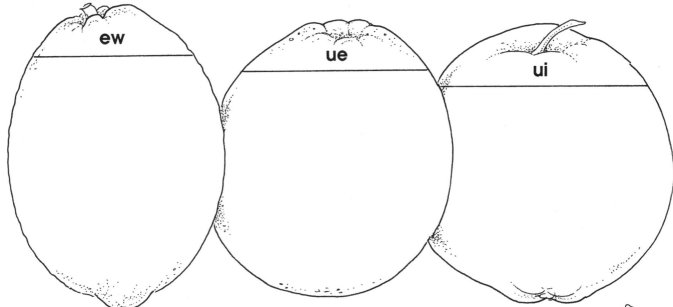

ew

ue

ui

3. **ue** is often at the **end** of words of more than one syllable.
   Put the right word by its meaning.

Tree-lined road          _____          continue

Moral excellence         _____          issue

Follow, seek after       _____          value

To set free              _____          avenue

Not stop, carry on       _____          virtue

Moulded figure           _____          pursue

The worth of something   _____          rescue

Thin paper for drying    _____          statue

One of a regular series  _____          tissue

Name _____     Date _____

# Spell aw au our words

There are a number of ways of spelling the **or** sound.

'The cat hurt its **paw**.'  'The **poor** cat was sad.'
'I will **pour** it some milk in a **saucer**.'

1. Read these words.

| | | | | | |
|---|---|---|---|---|---|
| lawn | awful | drawer | law | shawl | dawn |
| daughter | pause | August | source | saucer | haul |
| course | mourn | tour | cause | fourth | your |

2. Sort the words into the three balloons according to whether they have
   **aw**, **au**, or **our** in them.

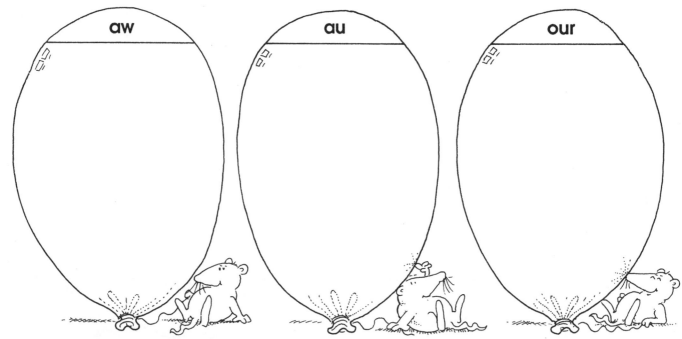

aw        au        our

3. **our** sometimes says **er**, as in 'col**our**'.
   Read these words.
   Note carefully if the word has **our**, or **o**. Often the **u** is dropped.

behaviour;  rumour;   harbour;  splendour;   endeavour;
odour - deodorant;  vapour - vaporise;
humour - humorous;  labour - laboratory;
vigour - vigorous;  glamour - glamorous;
colour - colourful; honour - honorary - honourable.

Turn over and spell these 'our', and 'or' words.
Check back to see if you are right.

Name _____ Date _____

# Negative prefixes

A **negative prefix** changes the meaning of a word to its opposite.

| dis | + | like | = dislike

Common negative prefixes are **un-**, **mis-**, **in-** and **dis-**.

You do **not** change the spelling of a word when you add a prefix to it.
The `in-` prefix has certain rules:

| | | | |
|---|---|---|---|
| **in-** becomes **im-** in front of b, m or p. | | | 'impossible'. |
| **in-** becomes **il-** in front of l. | | | 'illegal'. |
| **in-** becomes **ir-** in front of r. | | | 'irregular'. |

1. Read these words.

| untrue | discolour | misprint | irregular | mistreat | irrelevant |
| mislead | inactive | unknown | uncomfortable | uncertain | disappear |
| disobey | misplace | immortal | dishonest | impatient | unfortunate |
| invisible | untidy | discover | mistrust | disbelieve | |
| unkind | displace | mistake | illegible | misuse | |

2. Sort the words into four boxes according to what they begin with.

| un- | mis- | dis- | in-/im-/il-/ir- |

Some words start with **de-** or **des-** and can be confused with **dis-**.
Turn over and spell these common **des-** words to avoid confusion with **dis-**. Put each word into a sentence.

descend          despair          describe          destination

# Suffixes - general rules

A suffix is a letter, or group of letters put at the end of a word to change the way you use the word. The spelling of a suffix does not change, but the spelling of the word you add it to, sometimes does.

## 1
With words of one syllable, when there is one vowel before the single final consonant, double the consonant before adding the ending.
rub - **rubbed** - **rubbing** - **rubber** - **rubbery** - **rubbish**.

## 2
With words of one syllable, if a word has two vowels, or ends in two consonants, just add the suffix.
feel - **feeling**    kick - **kicked**
good - **goodness**

## 3
When a word ends in a 'magic' or 'lazy' e, drop the e before adding the ending, if the suffix begins with a vowel.
love - **loved** - **lovable** (*BUT lovely - loveless.*)

## 4
Words which end in soft c (ce) or soft g (ge), keep the e, to keep the c or g soft, when it is followed by a suffix beginning with a or o.
change - **changeable**
courage - **courageous**

## 5
Keep the e at the end of a word which ends in ye, oe, or ee.
how - **hoeing**    eye - **eyeing**
free - **freely**

## 6
When a word ends in y, it usually changes to i before adding the suffix, if there is a consonant before the y.
baby - **babies** beauty - **beautiful**
heavy - **heaviness**
(*BUT if the ending is ing, ist, or ish then keep the y so you don't have 'ii'.*)
cry - **crying** copy - **copyist**
baby - **babyish**

## 7
Words that have only one syllable usually keep the y.
fly - **flyer**    dry - **dryness**
(*BUT change the y to i before es and ed dry - dries, try - tried.*)

## 8
If there is a vowel before the y, keep the y before adding the suffix.
employ - **employing**
employment - **employable**
(*BUT day - daily, pay - paid, say - said, lay - laid.*)

## 9
When a word ends in ie, change the ie to y before adding ing.
die - **dying**    lie - **lying** tie - **tying**

## 10
Longer words (except words ending with 'l') with more than one syllable
sometimes follow the rules for one syllable words, **BUT** it depends how the word is pronounced.
a) If the stress in the word comes on the **first** syllable, you only have one consonant before the suffix.
offer - **offering**    gallop - **galloped**
b) If the stress in the word comes on the **second** syllable, you have two consonants before the suffix.
forbid - **forbidden** begin - **beginning**

## 11
Words ending in 'l'.
With words of more than one syllable which end in one 'l' after one vowel, you need to double the 'l' before adding a suffix beginning with a vowel.
travel - **traveller** signal - **signalling**
cancel - **cancellation**

Name _____  Date _____

# Spell -**tion** and -**sion** words

Many nouns end in **-ion**, in the form of **-ation**, **-ition**, **-sion**, or **-ssion**. When spelling a word ending like this, it may help to say the word to yourself and to listen out for **tion**, **ation**, **ition**, **ssion** ('sh' as in permi**ss**ion) or **sion** ('zh' as in televi**sion**).

## SOME HELP
a) Many words end in - **ation**.
   Many **ation** words come from verbs that end in -ate, -ite, or -ine. separate - **separation**.
b) **-ion** is less common. Some words end in **ction**, and some in **ition**. act - **action**; add - **addition**.
c) **-sion** is to do with verbs that end in **s, ade, ude, ede, ide, eed, ode,** or **it**. discuss - **discussion**; recede - **recession**; permit - **permission**.

1. Change these verbs into nouns by adding **ion**; **ation**; **ition**; **sion** or **ssion**.

| | | | |
|---|---|---|---|
| object | _____ | determine | _____ |
| oppose | _____ | elect | _____ |
| inform | _____ | impress | _____ |
| combine | _____ | educate | _____ |
| compose | _____ | possess | _____ |
| act | _____ | consider | _____ |
| explode | _____ | include | _____ |
| admit | _____ | populate | _____ |
| divide | _____ | conclude | _____ |

2. Choose five of these nouns. Turn over and put the five nouns into five sentences.

 Turn over and spell these words. Check back to see if you are right.

| | | |
|---|---|---|
| explain - explanation | repair - reparation | receive - reception |
| apply - application | destroy - destruction | exclaim - exclamation |
| despair - desperation | solve - solution | retain - retention |

# The 'ful' ending

When '**full**' is added to the end of a word, one '**l**' is dropped.

## SOME HELP

a)  If the word ends with an 'e', **keep the 'e' and add ful**.
    hope - **hopeful**.

b)  If the word has more than one syllable, and ends in a 'y' preceded
    by a consonant - **change the y to i and add ful**.
    pity - **pitiful**.

c)  If the word ends in oy or ay, **add ful**.
    joy - **joyful**.

1.  Make a list of words by adding **ful** and **fully** to these words.

| word | ful | fully |
|---|---|---|
| care | careful | carefully |
| peace | | |
| wonder | | |
| rest | | |
| power | | |
| thought | | |
| fancy | | |
| use | | |
| truth | | |
| forget | | |
| beauty | | |
| delight | | |
| play | | |
| fear | | |

*Note*:  awe - awful - awfully; skill - skilful - skilfully; will - wilful - wilfully.

2.  These adverbs say how somebody does something, or how something is
    done.  Put each one in a sentence to show its meaning.

cheerfully  _____

doubtfully  _____

sorrowfully  _____

successfully  _____

disgracefully  _____

Name _____    Date _____

# Spell -le -al -el words

**le** is the usual ending for short common words ending in an 'l' sound.
Longer words may take **al**, because in English you cannot have **mle**, **rle**,
or **nle**, nor **cle** if the c is 'soft'; **el** is not very common.

1. Read these words

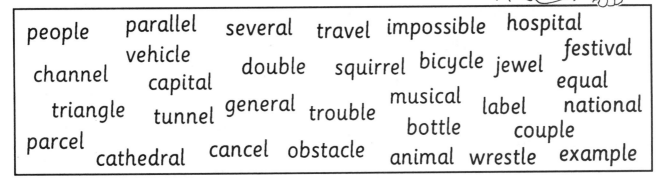

| people | parallel | several | travel | impossible | hospital |

people    parallel    several    travel    impossible    hospital
channel    vehicle    double    squirrel    bicycle    jewel    festival
capital    equal
triangle    tunnel    general    trouble    musical    label    national
bottle    couple
parcel    cathedral    cancel    obstacle    animal    wrestle    example

2. Sort the words into three boxes according to their endings.

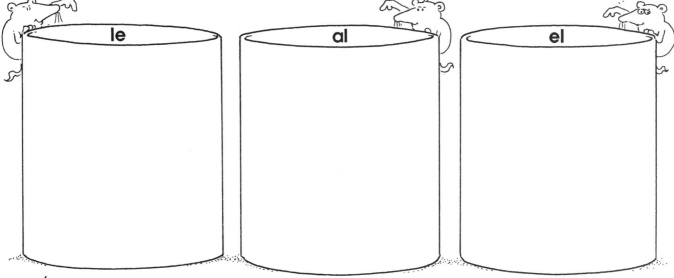

le          al          el

Many words end in **able**.
Put each of these words into a sentence.

suitable _____

reliable _____

valuable _____

reasonable _____

usable _____

# Spell -er-or-ar words

**er** is a very common word ending.
**or** and **ar** are less common, but they sound like **er**.
Look carefully.

1. Read these words:

| | | | | |
|---|---|---|---|---|
| doctor | exterior | shoulder | passenger | chapter |
| vinegar | author | familiar | visitor | conductor |
| surrender | powder | traitor | scholar | customer | peculiar |
| popular | calendar | explorer | messenger | operator |
| regular | grammar | burglar | mirror | terror | similar | conquer |

2. Sort the words into the three sacks according to their endings.

**er**        **or**        **ar**

 These three words end in ore. Look in a dictionary to find their meanings.

carnivore _____

herbivore _____

omnivore _____

Name _____   Date _____

# Spell -**ate** -**ite** -**ete** words

**ate** is a fairly common word ending.
**ite** and **ete** are less common.

1. Read these words.

athlete      illustrate        definite      incomplete

chocolate      desperate      deliberate      separate

favourite  polite   dynamite      complete   recite   fortunate

compete      decorate      demonstrate   investigate
climate

considerate   opposite  create      delete      educate

2. Sort the words into three boxes according to their endings.

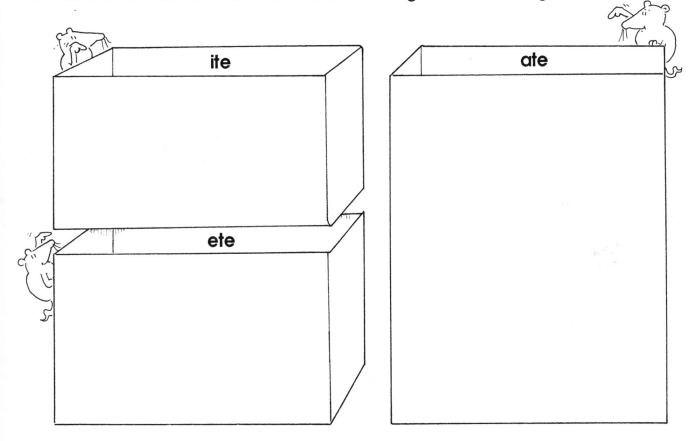

3. Use a dictionary to find the meanings of these four words. Write the
   meanings on the back of this sheet.
   exquisite, stagnate, negotiate, petite.

Name _____  Date _____

# Spell **-ary -ery -ory** words

These word endings can sound the same.
But **ary** is more common than **ery** or **ory**.
**ery** is often obvious when the word is spoken, and **ery** is usually added to a
'root' word: nurs**e** - nurs**ery**; pott**er** - pott**ery**.

1. Read these words:

| | | | |
|---|---|---|---|
| cookery | laboratory | jewellery | history |
| January | mystery | ordinary | boundary | machinery |
| story | glory | cemetery | extraordinary | factory | library |
| robbery | February | secretary | story | necessary |
| | bravery | victory | grocery | memory | dictionary |

2. Sort the words into the three jars according to their endings.

ary          ery          ary

 Do not confuse **stationary** and **stationery**.
Station**ary** means standing still.
Station**ery** means writing materials like paper,
(station**ery** and pap**er** both have **er**).

Name _____  Date _____

# Spell -ent and -ence words

ent and ence are more common than ant and ance.

The ending **ent** is usually used for adjectives.
The ending **ence** is usually used for nouns.

1. Here are some words which end in **ent** and **ence**.  Read the words.
Put them together in pairs on the lines.

silent _____    silence _____    different    obedience

_____    _____    confident    magnificence

_____    _____    violent    intelligence

_____    _____    absent    absence

_____    _____    obedient    convenience

_____    _____    magnificent    evidence

_____    _____    intelligent    ~~silence~~

_____    _____    ~~silent~~    difference

_____    _____    evident    violence

_____    _____    convenient    confidence

2. Put these adjectives into sentences.

frequent        _____

transparent    _____

decent          _____

recent          _____

detergent      _____

sufficient      _____

efficient       _____

Do not confuse 'license' and 'licence'.
Look the words up in a dictionary to find out
their meanings.

# Spell -**ant** and -**ance** words

**ant** and **ance** are not as common as **ent** and **ence**.

The ending   **ant**    is usually used for adjectives.
The ending   **ance**   is usually used for nouns.

1. Here are some words which end in **ant** and **ance**.
   Read the words.  Put them together in pairs on the lines.

| | |
|---|---|
| distant | distance |
| _____ | _____ |
| _____ | _____ |
| _____ | _____ |
| _____ | _____ |
| _____ | _____ |
| _____ | _____ |
| _____ | _____ |
| _____ | _____ |
| _____ | _____ |
| _____ | _____ |

| | |
|---|---|
| important | abundance |
| assistant | ignorance |
| abundant | fragrance |
| extravagant | arrogance |
| ignorant | defiance |
| fragrant | elegance |
| ~~distant~~ | importance |
| arrogant | assistance |
| elegant | extravagance |
| defiant | ~~distance~~ |

DEE ! DA !

2. Put these nouns into sentences.

appearance  _____

insurance  _____

ambulance  _____

acquaintance  _____

appliance  _____

romance  _____

Do not confuse `**currant**' and `**current**' -
and `**dependant**' and `**dependent**'.
Look the words up in a dictionary to find out their meanings.

Name _____ Date _____

# Odd words 1

1. In this puzzle colour the boxes which contain the names of **animals**. The words you have left are useful odd words to learn. Write these odd words on the lines underneath.

| bear | lettuce | jaguar | warm | usual | pig |
|---|---|---|---|---|---|
| else | lion | earth | search | tapir | type |
| ostrich | easy | straight | sheep | length | strength |
| instance | rabbit | monkey | pretty | donkey | busy |
| reindeer | reason | young | dog | method | mule |
| topic | cheetah | idea | recent | fox | damage |
| koala | region | million | yak | liquid | llama |
| various | giraffe | genuine | goat | cow | policy |
| horse | gigantic | antelope | notice | elephant | recipe |
| ferret | weasel | fraud | terrapin | theatre | tortoise |

_____  _____  _____  _____

_____  _____  _____  _____

_____  _____  _____  _____

_____  _____  _____  _____

_____  _____  _____  _____

_____  _____  _____  _____

_____  _____  _____  _____

2. What do these words have in common?

      deed        civic      gig

      rotator     poop     radar

They are all **palindromes**, which are words which can be spelt the same **backwards or forwards**. See if you can think of some more palindromes.

_____

_____

A sentence or a phrase can also be a palindrome. "Madam, I'm Adam."

Name _____    Date _____

# Odd words 2

1. In this puzzle colour the boxes which contain the names of **birds**. The words you have left are useful odd words to learn. Write these odd words on the lines underneath.

| | | | | |
|---|---|---|---|---|
| robin | fascinate | owl | special | terrific |
| figure | blackbird | temperature | wren | exaggerate |
| goose | rhyme | mystery | duck | fantastic |
| business | scheme | swan | cushion | finch |
| eagle | crow | voyage | hawk | opportunity |
| agenda | buzzard | individual | flamingo | imagine |
| swallow | anxious | coot | manoeuvre | vulture |
| familiar | sparrow | favourite | somersault | pheasant |
| stork | previous | lapwing | fashion | suitable |
| vehicle | pigeon | similar | falcon | description |
| warbler | library | heron | gradual | thrush |
| machine | kingfisher | eventually | puffin | brilliant |
| enthusiastic | auk | immediate | knowledge | cuckoo |

_____  _____  _____  _____

_____  _____  _____  _____

_____  _____  _____  _____

_____  _____  _____  _____

_____  _____  _____  _____

_____  _____  _____  _____

_____  _____  _____  _____

_____  _____  _____  _____

2. A **word square** can be made up of words of equal length that make words across and down.

```
C R A S H        S A G
H              A G E
H A N D        A G E T
A        N        G E T
I        D
R A F T S
```
or

A **word cross** is made up of two words which both have the same letter in the middle.

```
        B                    O
        L                    C
C L A I M      or   O C T O P U S
        C                    O
        K                    B
                             E
                             R
```

 Turn over and make up some word squares and word crosses.

# Difficult words!

Some of these words are tricky!  Study them carefully and use this page for reference.  Add your own to it!

## 1. **Single difficult words**

| | | | | |
|---|---|---|---|---|
| parliament | chrysalis | secretary | grandeur | schematic |
| government | analysis | appal | confectionery | confetti |
| privilege | recognise | control | fascinate | rhinoceroses |
| signature | coalesce | woollen | myrrh | synonymous |
| jeopardy | effervescence | suddenness | impetuous | margarine |
| satellite | allegiance | withhold | miscellaneous | paradigm |
| vacillate | ancillary | marriage | impostor | pandemonium |
| liaison | auxiliary | gauge | headache | rhapsody |
| fuchsia | anemone | gauze | acquaintance | immediately |
| occasion | fluorescent | murmur | deterrent | controversial |

My words:

_____

_____

## 2. **Confusing pairs of words (check the meanings!)**

| | | |
|---|---|---|
| practise/practice | gorilla/guerrilla | coarse/course |
| advise/advice | legible/eligible/illegible | principle/principal |
| affect/effect | lightning/lightening | licence/license |
| compliment/complement | gambol/gamble | currant/current |
| alter/altar | viscous/vicious | draft/draught |
| accept/except | story/storey | councillor/counsellor |
| allusion/illusion | lead/led | mettle/metal |
| quiet/quite | medal/meddle | diary/dairy |
| | conscious/conscience | |

My words:

_____

_____

## 3. **Some words change as their usage changes**

| | | | | |
|---|---|---|---|---|
| sustain | - sustenance | benefit | - benefited | |
| maintain | - maintenance | commit | - committed - commitment |
| abstain | - abstinence | occur | - occurrence | |
| argue | - argument | confer | - conference | |
| develop | - development | omit | - omitted | |
| disaster | - disastrous | limit | - limited | |
| fridge | - refrigerator | message | - messenger | |
| temporary | - temporarily | pronounce | - pronunciation |
| enemy | - enmity | | |

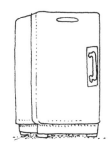

My words:

_____

_____

# Words from Book 1

| | | | | |
|---|---|---|---|---|
| at | job | glue | kick | foot |
| can | cup | play | lock | eyes |
| mad | gum | slip | neck | nose |
| wag | run | twig | all | hand |
| hen | hut | stop | seen | body |
| bet | brick | swim | too | arm |
| led | drop | spot | book | head |
| yes | free | smell | good | ear |
| fit | Gran | snip | snowman | mouth |
| did | crab | skull | window | |
| him | press | shot | mate | |
| zip | trip | chop | note | |
| dog | black | thin | ride | |
| hot | clap | wheel | tube | |
| fox | flat | sack | leg | |

*100 most used words in English ** 

| | | | | |
|---|---|---|---|---|
| a | down | little | other | two |
| about | first | look | out | up |
| all | for | made | right | want |
| an | from | make | said | was |
| and | get | me | see | we |
| are | go | more | she | well |
| as | had | much | so | went |
| at | has | must | some | were |
| back | have | my | that | what |
| be | her | new | the | when |
| been | he | no | their | where |
| before | here | not | them | which |
| big | him | now | then | who |
| but | his | of | there | will |
| by | I | off | they | with |
| call | if | old | this | you |
| came | in | on | to | your |
| can | into | one | | |
| come | is | only | | |
| could | it | or | **\* Source:** J. McNally and |
| did | just | our | W. Murray, *Key* |
| do | like | over | *Words to Literacy.* |

# Words from Book 2

| | | | |
|---|---|---|---|
| after | climb | morning | use |
| again | does | mother | usual |
| along | done | move | walk |
| always | every | nothing | water |
| animal | fast | once | while |
| another | father | open | why |
| any | friend | people | wonderful |
| around | give | please | word |
| ask | going | police | would |
| away | gone | pull | wrong |
| because | great | put | year |
| between | guess | shall | yet |
| biscuit | happy | should | young |
| break | island | sugar | yourself |
| brought | know | sure | zero |
| brother | last | talk | |
| build | live | thank | |
| buy | love | thought | |
| children | many | through | |

| | | | |
|---|---|---|---|
| splash | wheel | badge | action |
| string | apple | point | enormous |
| looked | might | enjoy | adventure |
| looking | farm | church | |
| shopped | horse | first | |
| shopping | team | cell | |
| liked | match | gem | |
| liking | cloud | half | |
| tent | teacher | knot | |
| lamp | oat | lamb | |
| munch | train | write | |
| hand | day | undo | |
| crown | happy | recall | |

# Word list for Book 3

*This list is based on groups of words found in the first half of this book.*

| | | | |
|---|---|---|---|
| bird | slowly | table | hymn |
| nest | parallel | castle | autumn |
| beach | balance | hedgehog | bustle |
| crisp | necessary | happy | listen |
| cake | comedy | pleased | wrap |
| sandwich | compartment | jolly | wreck |
| dinner | obstacle | glad | knee |
| broke | objection | overjoyed | knot |
| chase | obvious | bow | gnat |
| growl | adventure | arrow | gnome |
| drop | advertisement | flow | yacht |
| stare | condition | slow | cupboard |
| run | concentration | know | answer |
| snap | production | grow | half |
| scream | professionally | queen | |
| silky | excellent | quite | |
| dark | expensive | squid | |
| shiny | dogs | square | |
| noisy | foxes | cheque | |
| quiet | lorries | antique | |
| smiling | monkeys | elephant | |
| welcoming | shelves | triumph | |
| however | radios | feather | |
| although | potatoes | head | |
| until | women | heavy | |
| around | men | ready | |
| against | children | guitar | |
| below | feet | guide | |
| behind | teeth | honest | |
| between | picture | Christmas | |
| across | lighthouse | bomb | |
| suddenly | punchbag | climb | |
| gently | saucer | scissors | |
| wisely | luggage | science | |

# Word list for Book 3

*This list is based on groups of words found in the second half of this book.*

| | | | |
|---|---|---|---|
| mother | deceive | general | lettuce |
| father | either | principal | usual |
| sister | neither | principle | enormous |
| brother | reign | powder | special |
| son | rein | customer | chrysalis |
| daughter | chief | mirror | privilege |
| aquarium | field | visitor | parliament |
| aquatic | view | calendar | government |
| aqueduct | friend | grammar | jeopardy |
| antiseptic | grew | omnivore | privilege |
| antisocial | knew | councillor | maintenance |
| drastic | clue | counsellor | allegiance |
| frantic | glue | chocolate | anemone |
| trumpet | fruit | climate | satellite |
| ballet | suit | polite | fuchsia |
| souvenir | lawn | definite | |
| moustache | draw | complete | |
| cafe | pause | delete |  |
| restaurant | haunt | ordinary | |
| piano | course | boundary | |
| tobacco | mourn | mystery | |
| soprano | untrue | cookery | |
| pyjamas | mislead | story | |
| bazaar | disobey | factory | |
| bungalow | descend | century | |
| toboggan | objection | distant | |
| judo | question | distance | |
| tomahawk | explanation | currant | |
| borough | careful | current | |
| enough | peaceful | dependant |  |
| bought | beautiful | dependent | |
| brought | awful | silent | |
| laugh | couple | silence | |
| through | trouble | license | |
| receive | capital | licence | |

# APPENDIX

## Books

1. Alston, J. and Taylor, J. *The Handwriting File*. L.D.A.
2. Bissex, G.L. (1980) *Gnys at Wrk*. Harvard University Press.
3. Brown and Brown (1990) *A Speller's Companion*. Reed's Ltd. Penrith.
4. Bryant, P.E. and Bradley, L. (1985) *Children's Reading Problems*. Blackwell.
5. Daniels, J.C. and Diack, H. (1979) *The Standard Reading Tests*. Hart-Davis.
6. Gee, R. and Watson, C. (1990) *English Spelling*. Usborne.
7. Gentry, J.R. (1987) *SPEL .... is a four letter word*. Scholastic.
8. Marsh, E. (1989) *Help yourself to English Spelling*. Oriflamme.
9. McNally, B. and Murray, W. (1970) *Key Words to Literacy*. The Teacher Publishing Company, Northants.
10. National Curriculum Documents (1989) *English in the National Curriculum*. H.M.S.O.
11. Peters, M.L. (1975) *Diagnostic and Remedial Spelling Manual*. Macmillan.
12. Schonell, F.J. (1976) *Graded Word Spelling Test*. L.D.A.
13. Torbe, M. (1977) *Teaching Spelling*. Ward Lock Ed.
14. Vernon, P.E. (1977) *Spelling Test*. NFER/ Nelson.
15. Vincent, D. and Claydon, J. (1982) *Diagnostic Spelling Test*. NFER/Nelson.

## Dictionaries and Thesauri

1. *A.C.E. Dictionary* (Aurally Coded English) L.D.A. (Words are found according to their sound.)
2. Beeching, C.L. (1989) *A Dictionary of Eponyms*. Oxford University Press.
3. Cohen, J.M. and Cohen, M.J. (1960) *Dictionary of Quotations*. Penguin.
4. Cripps, C. and Peters, M.L. (1991) *Hands on Spelling Dictionary*. L.D.A.
5. Fergusson, R. (1984) *The Penguin Rhyming Dictionary*. Penguin.
6. Fowler, H.W. and Fowler, F.C. (1989) *The Concise Oxford Dictionary*. Oxford.
7. Grisewood, J. (1990) *Fact File Dictionary*. W. H. Smith.
8. Hawkins, J.M. (1991) *New Oxford School Dictionary*. Oxford University Press.
9. *Pergamon Dictionary of Perfect Spelling*. Pergamon (This dictionary shows correct spellings alongside likely misspellings.)
10. *Pocket Thesaurus*. (1984) Kingfisher Books.
11. Roget, P.M. (1933 edition) *Thesaurus - Classic Edition*. Avenel Books, New York.
12. Spooner A. (1987) *Oxford Children's Thesaurus*. Sphere Books.
13. *The Young People's Thesaurus Dictionary*. Ward Lock Ed.

## Spelling programmes

1. *Attack* spelling programme (100 systematically structured spelling lessons) Richards, J. P.B.S. Nottingham.
2. *Catchwords - Ideas for Teaching Spelling*. (A set of six graded workbooks.) Cripps, C. (1978) Harcourt, Brace, Jovanovich.
3. Hornsby, and Shear, F. (1976) *Alpha to Omega*. Heinemann.
4. *Spelling Made Easy*. Brand V. Egon Publishers Ltd.
5. *Stile Spelling Programme*. (Self-correcting spelling programme for 5-14-year-olds.) L.D.A.

## Spellchecker

*Franklin Elementary Spellmaster* (QES90). (Designed for children with 26,800 words in it.) Innovations International Ltd., Richmond, Surrey.

## Computer programs

1. *Short Vowel Sounds. Magic e. Consonant Blends. Vowel digraphs. Word Builder.* Five programs to help with phonics. Sherston Software, Malmesbury, Wilts.
2. *Spelling Week by Week.* Six Levels cover the ages 5-11. The computer monitors and scores levels for each child. Chalksoft Ltd., P.O.Box 49, Spalding.
3. *Star Spell* (for younger children) and *Star Spell Plus* (for older children). Fisher Marriot, Lower Fulbrook, Warwick.